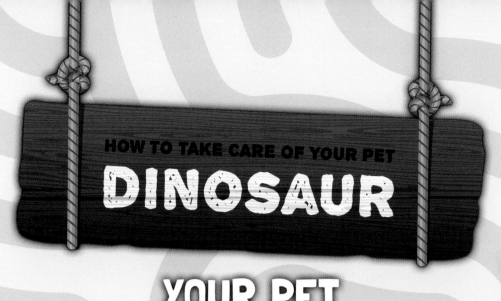

HOW TO TAKE CARE OF YOUR PET
DINOSAUR

YOUR PET
TYRANNOSAURUS REX

By Kirsty Holmes

THE OFFICIAL
F.O.S.S.I.L
GUIDE

BookLife
PUBLISHING

©2018
BookLife Publishing
King's Lynn
Norfolk PE30 4LS

All rights reserved.
Printed in Malaysia.

A catalogue record for this book is
available from the British Library.

ISBN: 978-1-78637-486-8

Written by:
Kirsty Holmes

Edited by:
Madeline Tyler

Designed by:
Danielle Jones

All facts, statistics, web addresses
and URLs in this book were verified
as valid and accurate at time of
writing. No responsibility for any
changes to external websites or
references can be accepted by
either the author or publisher.

IMAGE CREDITS

Cover – solar22, Bibela, ONYXprj, stuckmotion, isaree, Kurt Natalia. 1 & throughout – stuckmotion, solar22. 4 – Mountain Brothers. 5 – Sentavi.
8 – VectoRaith. 9 – Viktorija Reuta, TopVectorElements. 10 – HstrongART. 11 – sivVector, Bahruz Rzayev, callz76. 12 – Teguh Mujiono. 13 – Iconic Bestiary,
RoseRodionova. 14 – Studio_G. 15 – Dimonika. 17 – hanna kutsybala, SaveJungle. 18 – Top Vector Studio. 20 – Inspiring. 21 – Zhenyakot, pupahava, AlexHliv.
22 – Oleksandr Derevianko, Panda Vector. Images are courtesy of Shutterstock.com. With thanks to Getty Images, Thinkstock Photo and iStockphoto.

CONTENTS

THE OFFICIAL FOSSIL GUIDE

Words that look like this can be found in the glossary on page 24.

F.O.S.S.I.L

So, you're the proud owner of a dinosaur egg. Congratulations!

Owning a pet dinosaur is a lot of hard work, but it's worth the trouble. Dinosaurs make excellent pets.

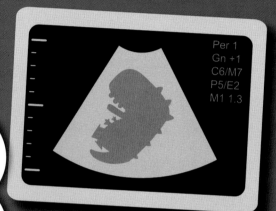

Per 1
Gn +1
C6/M7
P5/E2
M1 1.3

CONGRATULATIONS! IT'S A... TYRANNOSAURUS REX!

If you are a first-time dinosaur owner, you probably have lots of questions. Never fear! This handy F.O.S.S.I.L guide will tell you all you need to know.

F.O.S.S.I.L
FACT

F.O.S.S.I.L stands for:

Federal
Office of
Super
Sized
Interesting
Lizards

EGGS

Tyrannosaurus (also known as T. rex) eggs are long, thin and oval. They are about 30 centimetres (cm) long.

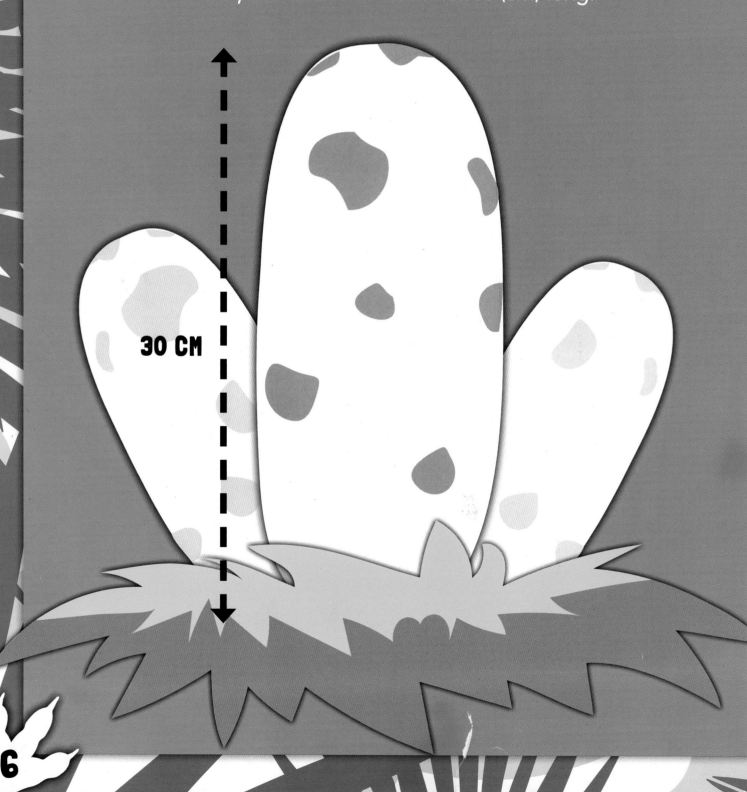

30 CM

T. rex eggs should stay quite warm. Build a round <u>nest</u> in the garden and cover your egg with leaves and soil to protect it.

BABIES

Your baby T. rex might hatch from its egg covered with fluffy feathers. Make sure to dry it off thoroughly.

THE FEATHERS MAY HELP TO KEEP THE BABY WARM.

Feed your baby T. rex lots of small pieces of raw meat. Wear strong gloves – your pet isn't trained yet and might try and nip your fingers.

GROWTH

Your T. rex will grow slowly and steadily for the first few years. As it grows, it will lose its feathers and become more scaly.

— ONE YEAR OLD

TWO YEARS OLD

F.O.S.S.I.L FACT

Keep an eye on any other pets. T. rex loves to play!

Adults can grow as long as 13 metres (m), from nose to tail.
Make sure you have somewhere suitable for your pet to sleep.

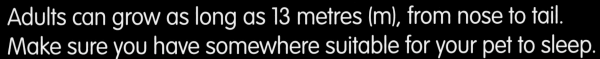

F.O.S.S.I.L FACT

A fully-grown T. rex can weigh 6,000 kilograms (kg)!

BEWARE OF THE T. REX

FOOD

Tyrannosaurs are <u>carnivores</u>. They have sharp, pointy teeth, which are shaped like cones. The teeth can be up to 23 cm long and are for tearing up its favourite food: meat!

F.O.S.S.I.L FACT

T. rex has a big <u>appetite</u>. Don't let it eat your neighbour's pets – or your <u>siblings</u>!

In the wild, T. rex would have been an amazing predator. As a pet, it is better to use special pet food – it's not a good idea to let your T. rex go hunting in your neighbourhood.

EXERCISE

Your T. rex will probably sleep a lot – especially after a big meal. If your pet is full, it's best to let it sleep it off.

DIPPYSTRIPZ

DIPPYSTRIPZ

Don't let your pet sleep all the time. T. rex still needs to exercise. Luckily for you, T. rex isn't very fast, and you should easily be able to keep up.

F.O.S.S.I.L FACT
You will need a long lead – T. rex can be up to 6 m tall!

NAMING

Naming your T. rex is very important when <u>bonding</u> with your pet. You could choose to use part of the Tyrannosaur's name as a nickname.

REX

F.O.S.S.I.L FACT

What will you name your T. rex?

You could use words that describe your T. rex to name it instead. T. rex is large and fierce, with snappy teeth.

IT CAN BE FUN TO GIVE YOUR PET AN UNEXPECTED NAME INSTEAD.

FLUFFY!

WASHING

Pets must be kept clean and well-groomed. It is especially important to brush your T. rex's teeth. To do this safely, you will need:

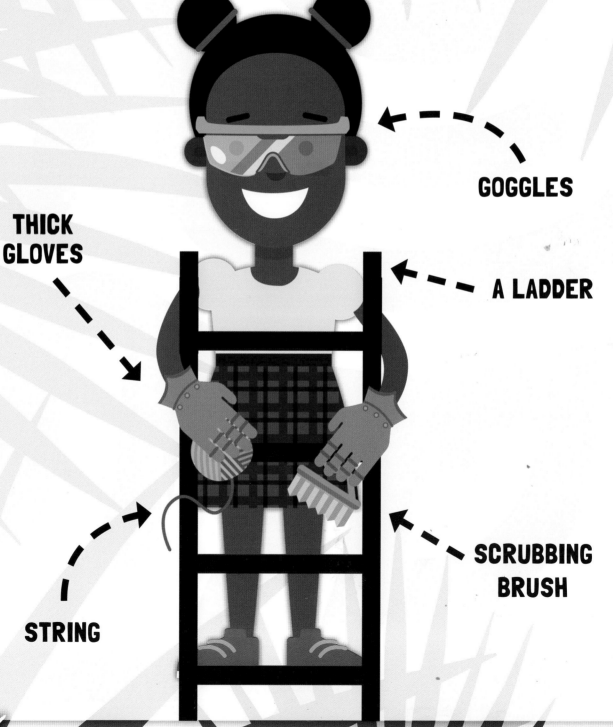

GOGGLES

THICK GLOVES

A LADDER

SCRUBBING BRUSH

STRING

Make sure your T. rex is not hungry before cleaning its teeth. Then carefully clean each tooth. It is not recommended to put your arm inside the mouth… just in case.

F.O.S.S.I.L
FACT

Carnivores can have very bad breath. <u>Floss</u> carefully to get all the little bits of meat out.

PROBLEMS

When keeping a dangerous pet, it is important to make sure your home is <u>secure</u>. A T. rex on the loose in the streets could cause a panic.

IF YOUR T. REX ESCAPES, WE RECOMMEND YOU CALL THE F.O.S.S.I.L EMERGENCY LINE ON 65 000 000.

Cleaning up after your pet can be challenging. An average pooper scooper will not be up to the job. Make sure you have the right equipment.

TRICKS

T. rex is quite clever and has a large brain. Your pet will love learning new tricks.

DON'T PLAY FETCH IN A CROWDED AREA. PEOPLE COULD GET SWATTED BY T. REX'S LONG TAIL.

GLOSSARY

APPETITE   how much you want or need to eat

BONDING   forming a close relationship

CARNIVORES   animals that eat other animals rather than plants

FLOSS   thin string used to clean between teeth

NEST   any place used by an animal to lay eggs or rear young

PREDATORS   animals that hunt other animals for food

SECURE   protected so that nothing can get in or out

SIBLINGS   brothers and/or sisters

INDEX